Helping Kids Recognize Emotions and Express Feelings

MY BODY SENDS
A SIGNAL

Written by
Natalia Maguire

Illustrated by
Anastasia Zababashkina

ISBN: 978-3-9821428-3-8

For more information please contact
Natalia Magvayr
Maguire Books
Parkstrasse 8, 22605 Hamburg, Germany

Visit our website at: www.maguirebooks.com

First printed and bound in the USA.

Dear Grown-up,

I am delighted that you are passionate about making your children more confident, enabling them to build stronger relationships as well as to perform better academically. These abilities require "emotional regulation"— that is, the process of recognizing emotions, expressing feelings, calming oneself down in the face of overwhelming emotions, and learning to treat others with empathy.

Like us, adults, kids have a wide range of feelings. They get happy, jealous, disgusted, angry, nervous, sad, proud, worried, and excited. But at a very young age, they simply don't possess the vocabulary to express their feelings verbally. They express their feelings through tantrums, mimicry, physical movements, and gestures. These expressions are often sweet and funny, but sometimes they just drive us nuts!

This book will help you explain to your kids that emotions, that is signals they get from their bodies, are linked to feelings. These feelings, whether positive or negative, are all perfectly fine, but they can be expressed differently.

This book will also expand your children's vocabulary by offering them different words to express their feelings with.

And finally, the book offers hands-on activities for hours of entertainment after reading.

I hope your kids will enjoy the story.

I feel...

EXCITED.

Yours,

Natalia Maguire

3

boom

boom

brrr-brrr

My body sends me so many signals to tell me how I feel. Sometimes I sweat, my stomach rumbles, it's hard to breathe, my heart races like crazy. Sometimes I want to jump for joy, and then I want to yell or cry.

But why? Why? Why?

One day my Mom said: "I have a nice surprise for you! But you have to wait until lunch."

What could it be? I just couldn't wait.

I walked around the house, unable to concentrate on anything. I started playing with my blocks, but my brain just wouldn't stop thinking about the surprise long enough to build a tall castle. Then, I got my train set out, but for some reason the choo choo just wasn't much fun. Next, I tried to use my toy tools to build the best race car ever, but my brain kept wondering about the surprise Mom had for me.

My heart beat faster and faster.

My skin tingled.

I felt ants in my pants.

I was so EXCITED!

6

Mom hugged me. "Not long to wait," she said.

7

And then I heard the doorbell. Mom looked at me, smiling. "Do you want to open the door?" She asked.

I rushed to the door and opened it wide.

There, with their arms open wide to hug me, stood Grandma and Grandpa!

"Surprise!" Grandma said with a big smile. "Who is this big man?"

My eyes shined.

A wide smile lit up my face.
I jumped for joy!

I was so HAPPY!

My Grandpa asked me to show him what I had learned in school.
I showed him the letters that I had learned to write, the books that
I'd read with Mom, and the pictures that I had drawn.
And then, I handed him the dragon, I had created from
soft clay the other day.

"It's a present for you, Grandpa!" I told him.
"Do you like it?"

"Like it?" He exclaimed. "I **LOVE** it! It's a
piece of art!"

10

I stood up straight.
I held my head up.
My eyes shined.

I felt very PROUD of myself!

The next day the weather was perfect for a day out, and we went to the zoo. The sun was shining bright, and all the animals were enjoying the perfect day.

First, we went to the tigers. We were standing behind a large glass wall so we could see them clearly. A big tiger was lying just in front of us. He seemed to be asleep, or maybe just relaxing in the sun.

Two boys, who were standing beside me, decided to annoy the tiger. They were screaming, knocking on the glass, and making faces.
Until suddenly ... the tiger jumped up right in front of us and growled menacingly.

13

BOOM

BOOm

My heart jumped.

My knees shook.
My legs got weak.

14

I felt pain in my stomach.

I wanted to hide.

I was so SCARED!

My Grandma quickly pulled me back and hugged me.

"It is ok to be scared," said Grandma. "I was frightened too."

I breathed out.
My heart felt normal again.
My knees weren't so wobbly anymore.
I calmed down.

It felt SAFE.

My misfortunes did not end there. As we walked out of the tigers' enclosure, I smelled an awful smell. "Where was it coming from?" I wondered. And then I looked down and saw that I had stepped in a squishy, stinky poo!!!! "Ugh!" I exclaimed.

My nose wrinkled up.
My upper lip curled.

My head shook from side to side.
My mouth got all watery, and
I thought I might throw up.

I was so DISGUSTED!

Grandpa stroked my back.
"Oh, dear," he said.
"Let's go clean it."

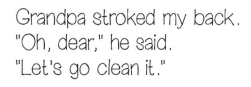

19

This was the last straw. I no longer wanted
to go see other animals. I wanted to go home.
What an awful day!

20

I tried to stop it, but
my bottom lip just couldn't
help but stick way out there.

My whole body felt down.
My eyes felt watery. I was
going to cry.

I was very SAD.

When we got home, things only got worse.

It appears, my sister decided to play with the robot that my Granny and Granddad had brought me. She dropped it from the table, it cracked and stopped working.

I just couldn't bear it anymore.

My hands clenched.

My shoulders tensed up.

I pushed my sister
and kicked that stupid table.
And I started to yell.

I felt so ANGRY.

"Oh, my darling," Mom said and hugged
me. "I understand that you are upset.
You have the right to be angry."

I think you should take some time to cool down. And then we will discuss how we can fix your robot." And then Mom took me to my room.

25

Later, Mom called me to come down for dinner.
I did not really want to eat.

26

My cheeks turned red.
I felt very hot.

My hands were trembling.
I could not raise my head
and look into my Granny's eyes.

I was so ASHAMED of my behavior.

27

"I am very sorry," I said.

Grandma hugged me, looked into my eyes, and said, "You had the right to be angry. And you needed to let off some steam. But it is not ok to yell and kick. You can control your anger instead of letting it control you.

I can teach you some ways to do it:

28

First, take ten very deep breaths—slowly breathe in through your nose and breathe out through your mouth while counting 1, 2, 3, 4, 5, 6, 7, 8, 9, 10.

Instead of throwing or kicking things because of anger, just squeeze this anger in your hands and hold it there tightly. Then, let it go.

Instead of yelling or saying bad words, just say, "I am very angry!"

Instead of hitting someone, just walk away.

Don't' let your anger be your boss! Do you promise to try this next time?"

"Yes," I nodded.

"I know you will," said Grandma and kissed me. "You are such a smart boy. I love you!"

The next morning, I slept late. Mom did not wake me up. She probably wanted me to recover from all the stress I'd had the day before. On the way to the living room, I heard a familiar noise. I immediately understood what it was.

I rushed into the room. Yes! I was right—my Granddad was sitting on the floor, and the robot was walking in front of him.

I could not believe my eyes!

My eyebrows raised.
My eyes opened wide.

My mouth opened.

I was totally SURPRISED!

Granddad laughed. "See, I fixed it! It was just a small thing, nothing serious. So, here. It's working perfectly again."

I rushed to Grandpa and hugged him tightly. And then I did a funny dance around the robot.

I was FILLED WITH JOY!

Each day my body sends me a lot of signals.

All these signals have meaning.

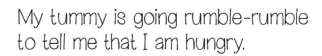

My tummy is going rumble-rumble to tell me that I am hungry.

My mouth gets dry to tell me I am thirsty, and it's time to drink some water.

I yawn when I am tired or bored.

I get goosebumps when I get cold.

I sweat when I am hot.

I get butterflies in my stomach when I am nervous.

I get so many of these feelings!

And they are all PERFECTLY FINE!

Do you remember being scared or ashamed, sad or happy?

Share your story with me!
Ask your parents or your teacher to help you find the right words!

I feel happy!
I am glad.
I am cheerful.
I am delighted.
I feel terrific.

I feel proud!
I am delighted with myself.

I am surprised.
I am amazed.
I am astonished.
I am shocked.

I am ashamed.
I am disappointed with myself.

I am sad.
I am upset.
I am very down.
I am unhappy.
I feel miserable.

Dear Grown-up,

Upon completing the story, consider playing a game with your child. Below you will find:

Emotions Cards — pictures of emotions,

Feelings Cards — cards with images of feelings,

Short Stories — texts that describe situations where feelings and emotions may occur.

Coloring pages

Start with Emotions Cards and Feelings Cards
Place the Emotions Cards and the Feelings Cards on the table. Ask your child to link the emotions (signals our bodies send us) with feelings (the meanings these signals have). You can use the book to check and see if you are matching them correctly. However, these connections vary from person to person, as all of us experience emotions differently.

Continue with Short Stories.
Read the short stories and discuss with your child how the children, described in these stories, might be feeling. Find the related Feelings Cards and Emotions Cards. If you are playing with more than one child, let them take turns. Motivate the kids to use synonyms to describe each feeling.

Take it further. Place the Feelings Cards in front of your child and ask to come up with stories pertaining to instances when the feeling on the card may occur.

Have fun!

Please visit www.maguirebooks.com to download the cards and the coloring pages as .pdf files.

MY HEART BEATS
FASTER AND FASTER.

MY SKIN TINGLES.

I FEEL ANTS IN MY PANTS.

MY EYES SHINE.

A WIDE SMILE LITS UP MY FACE.

I JUMP FOR JOY!

I STAND UP STRAIGHT.

I HOLD MY HEAD UP.

MY HEART JUMPS.

MY KNEES SHAKE.

MY LEGS GET WEAK.

I FELL PAIN IN MY STOMACH.

I WANT TO HIDE.

I BREATHE OUT.

MY KNEES AREN'T
WODBLY ANYMORE.

I CALM DOWN.

MY NOSE WRINKLES UP.

MY UPPER LIP CURLS.

MY HEAD SHAKES SIDE-TO-SIDE.

MY MOUTH GETS ALLWATERY,
AND I THINK I MIGHT THROW UP.

MY BOTTOM LIP STICKS WAY OUT.

MY WHOLE BODY FEELS DOWN.

MY EYES FEEL WATERY.
I AM GOING TO CRY.

MY HANDS CLENCH.

MY SHOULDERS TENSE UP.

I WANT TO KICK AND TO YELL.

MY CHEEKS TURN RED.

I FEEL VERY HOT.

MY HANDS ARE TREMBLING.

I CAN'T RAISE MY HEAD AND
LOOK INTO OTHER PEOPLE'S EYES.

MY EYEBROWS RAISE.

MY EYES OPEN WIDE.
MY MOUTH OPENS WIDE.

HAPPY

PROUD

SCARED

SAFE

SAD

DISGUSTED

ANGRY

ASHAMED

EXCITED

SURPRISED

HUNGRY

BORED

NERVOUS

JEALOUS

CONFUSED

SHY

SHORT STORIES

Mark liked to play with sand and build sandcastles. His dad bought him a toy truck that could deliver sand to the castle building site. Mark was very proud of his truck. One day, as he played on the beach, a boy came up to him, smashed his castle, and took away his truck. When Mark tried to get it back, the boy wouldn't let him and tried to kick Mark.

How do you think Mark felt? He was . . .

angry

Felix and John were brothers who loved to play ball. But their Mom always asked them not to play in the house.

"You can play with the ball when we go for a walk," she always said. "In the house, you might break something."

One day, Mom was busy cooking while Felix and John were alone in the living room.

"Let's play with the ball while Mom isn't looking," suggested John.

"But not too loud, ok?" agreed Felix.

So, they played. The boys imagined they were playing in a cup final. Until . . . the ball hit Mom's favorite vase that was standing on a sideboard next to the sofa. The vase fell and broke into small pieces.

Mom heard the noise and rushed into the room.

How do you think Felix and John felt? They were . . .

ashamed

Kathy's class was learning about insects, so they went to visit the zoo. First, they went to the butterfly garden. All the butterflies were beautiful, but they tried to avoid landing on Kathy's hands. It was a bit upsetting.

Then, the class went to see spiders. They were not beautiful at all. In fact, they were horrid. One of them was particularly big and hairy.

"Would you like to touch it?" asked the teacher with a smile on her face.

"No!" exclaimed the kids, and they all stepped back.

The kids were . .

disgusted

In the morning, Carla just did not want to eat.

"You will regret not having a proper breakfast," Mom said. "We are going for a long walk in the park."

But Carla refused to eat.

The walk in the park was great. Carla met her friends, Sam and Jack, and they played hide-and-seek together. When it was Carla's turn to hide, she decided to go behind the hotdog stand beside the playground. As Carla was hiding, her stomach started to growl. The tasty smell of sausages and bread rolls was all she could think about.

What feeling did Carla have? Carla was . . .

hungry

Ivan was a great runner. When his Mom heard about a running competition for kids, she immediately told Ivan.

"I think you should try it. You love running, don't you?" Mom said.

Ivan was very excited to compete. Every day he asked his Dad to take him for a little run so that he would be well prepared. Finally, it was the day of the big race. Ivan woke up early, did some stretching exercises, ate a healthy breakfast, and put on his running gear. He was all set to do well. But could he win?

Ivan ran as quickly as he could. He heard kids running behind him and felt that any minute someone would overtake him. But they didn't. Now, Ivan could see the finish line. Was he going to win? Ivan was just several meters away from the line when he suddenly fell. Ivan felt an intense pain in his left ankle and could not stand up. All he could do was see another boy win the race and jump for joy.

How do you think Ivan felt? Ivan was . . .

sad

Sam and Lilly couldn't wait for the morning to come. It was Christmas Eve, and they were hoping to get presents from Santa Claus. They both had sent letters to him. Sam asked for a remote-control car, and Lilly asked for a new bicycle. When Sam woke up in the morning, he rushed to wake up Lilly.

"Lilly, quickly, wake up! The presents must be there!" he exclaimed. He did not have to ask twice.

Lilly immediately stood up, and both Sam and Lilly rushed to the Christmas tree.

How do you think Sam and Lilly felt? They were . . .

excited

"Mom's birthday is in two weeks," said Dad. "Do you have an idea for a present?"

Kate didn't. What would Mom like? Kate spent the whole evening brainstorming until finally, she had an idea. She remembered that in school they were learning to make flowers from fabrics. So, Kate decided to try and make a flower brooch for her Mom. She asked her Mom to give her some fabric leftovers. She found a broken brooch from which she could use a pin, and stayed in her room every evening, secretly crafting.

The brooch turned out very nice. Kate just couldn't wait to present it to her mom. She found a small box and decorated it nicely so that it looked like a real jewelry box. When Mom finally got the brooch, she could not believe her eyes.

"This is the most beautiful piece of jewelry I have ever had!" exclaimed Mom. "And it matches my dress just perfectly! I have to wear it right away!"

How do you think Kate felt? Kate was ...

proud

Tim had a friend named Peter. Peter lived just two houses away from Tim, so Tim's Mom allowed him to go visit his friend alone. One day Tim was returning home when he heard:

"Woof!"

Tim was rooted to the spot. He didn't know what to do. Slowly, he turned around. Behind him was a huge, ugly dog.

How do you think Tim felt? Tim was . . .

scared

66

Louis dreamt of having a dog. He kept asking for one, but Mom always refused.

"I have three kids and a husband. That's just enough for me!" said Mom.

So, Louis started to believe that he would never ever have a dog . . .

On the morning of his 7th birthday, he woke himself up. This was unusual because he was a long sleeper, and his Mom always struggled to wake him up. But not this time. Something had woken him. But what? Louis heard sounds near his bed, so he looked down to see what it was.

Beside his bed, in a little box, sat a beautiful, fluffy puppy. Louis just could not believe his eyes.

How do you think Louis was feeling? He was . . .

happy

It was Christmas Concert Day at school. Bill was given a leading role in the song that his class was singing. Bill learned all the words and felt confident.

However, as the kids got on stage, Bill got so frightened that he forgot all the words. The music started, and Bill was supposed to start singing, but he couldn't remember the words! The music stopped, then started again, but he stood there clueless about what to do. Bill did not remember the words!

Eventually, another boy from Bill's class came to the microphone and helped him sing.

After the concert, Bill was very . . .

ashamed and sad

It was report day at school. Alex got a sealed envelope from the teacher.

"This is your school report. Please bring it to your parents," the teacher said.

At home, Mom decided not to open the report herself, but to wait until the family sat down for dinner because she wanted to read it when everyone was around the table.

When dinner ended, Dad said, "It looks like the perfect time to see your school report, Alex. Can you bring it to me?"

Alex passed the report to his dad. He had butterflies in his stomach.

Alex was ...

excited/nervous

Dad started to read the report out loud:
"In Reading, Alex exceeds expectations! In Writing Alex . . .exceeds expectations! In Math, Alex . . . exceeds expectations!"

As Dad was reading it, Alex felt ...

proud

When Simon celebrated his birthday party, his Mom let him invite all the boys from his class to a party in the park. It was so much fun!

A month later, he noticed kids circulating invitations to Joe's party, and discussing how great that party would be. It seemed like almost all the boys in the class got invited to this party. All but Simon . . .

How do you think Simon felt? He was . . .

sad

Did you like our story? We would be DELIGHTED to hear from you.

Please leave a review!

CONFUSED

EXCITED

HAPPY

PROUD

SCARED

SAFE

DISGUSTED

SAD

LOVED

SURPRISED

FILLED WITH JOY

TIRED

Printed in Great Britain
by Amazon

80939586R00047